Preface

This is a workbook for teenage girls who have been sexually abused. It is written by two therapists and includes the writing and experiences of many of the young women we have worked with in individual and group therapy. The text explains what sexual abuse is and describes how it often affects teenagers who have been sexually abused. Throughout the workbook there are questions for you to answer and activities to help you explore how you have been affected by sexual abuse.

We have designed this workbook for you to use with a therapist in individual or group therapy. We believe that you need and deserve the support of a caring and trusted therapist when you begin to try to understand how sexual abuse has affected you.

Other teenage girls have dealt with the same issues that you face. We hope their words will help you realize that you are not alone and that there are other people who can understand what you have experienced. Through their example, we hope you will recognize that you can learn about and talk about your own sexual abuse, and grow to feel stronger, happier, and more in control of your own life.

Lulie and Karen

In Their Own Words

A Sexual Abuse Workbook for Teenage Girls

by

Lulie Munson
and Karen Riskin

Child Welfare League of America
Washington, DC

Child Welfare League of America, Inc.
440 First Street, NW, Suite 310, Washington, DC 20001–2085

Current Printing (last digit)
10 9 8 7 6 5 4 3

Cover and text design by Paul Butler

Printed in the United States of America

ISBN # 0–87868–596–0

Contents

Preface v

Acknowledgments vii

Introduction: How to Use This Workbook ix

Workbook Contract xi

Feelings List xiii

I. What Is Sexual Abuse? 1
How Do You Define Sexual Abuse? 1
Take a Break: Check In with Yourself 2
What Is Inappropriate Sexual Behavior? 2
Who Sexually Abuses Children? 3
You Are Not Alone 4
In Their Own Words 4
Suggested Activities 5

II. The Effects of Sexual Abuse 7
Sexual Abuse Is a Trauma 7
What Is Post-Traumatic Stress Disorder? 8
Take a Break: Check In with Yourself 9
Teenagers and Post-Traumatic Stress Disorder 10
In Their Own Words 10
Suggested Activities 11

III. It Takes Courage to Remember 13
What Triggers Your Memories? 14
Take a Break: Check In with Yourself 18
In Their Own Words 18
Suggested Activities 19

IV. Coping with Your Memories 21
Grounding 21
Flooding and Freezing 22
Where Are You on The Barometer Right Now? 23
Take a Vacation Break 23
In Their Own Words 27
Suggested Activities 27

V.	**Keeping the Secret**	29
	Why Does a Child Keep Sexual Abuse a Secret?	29
	Take a Break: Check In with Yourself	31
	Living with the Secret	31
	In Their Own Words	32
	Suggested Activities	33
VI.	**What Happens When You Tell**	35
	Trying to Tell	35
	What Happened When You Told?	37
	Take a Break: Check In with Yourself	38
	The Benefits and Difficulties of Telling	38
	Deciding to Tell	39
	In Their Own Words	40
	Suggested Activities	40
VII.	**Telling the Details**	41
	How Can Telling Help Me?	41
	Starting to Tell	42
	In Their Own Words	52
	Suggested Activities	52
VIII.	**Was It Your Fault?**	53
	"I Should Have"	53
	"What I Did Was Wrong"	54
	More about Blame	57
	In Their Own Words	58
	Suggested Activities	59
IX.	**It's OK to Have Feelings**	61
	Feelings Exercises	61
	Take A Break: Check in with Yourself	64
	More Exercises	64
	In Their Own Words	70
	Suggested Activities	72
X.	**Taking Charge of Your Life**	73
	Being Assertive	73
	Assertiveness Log	75
	Putting the Abuse in Its Place	76
	Recognizing Your Strengths	77
	Getting and Giving Support	78
	In Their Own Words	79
	Suggested Activities	79
	About the Authors	81

Acknowledgments

This workbook evolved during seven years of our work with sexually abused adolescent girls at the Germaine Lawrence School, a residential treatment program in Arlington, Massachusetts. Most of the activities and exercises in the book were initially developed in the Germaine Lawrence Survivors Group and then incorporated into individual and family therapy. The school's treatment philosophy, which emphasizes the importance of nurturance and structure and of teaching troubled adolescents the skills to take positive control of their lives, is embedded in these pages.

We would like to thank Alex Prior for her contribution to this workbook. Alex and Lulie Munson were the founders of the Survivors Group, and the group format that they designed has greatly influenced the content of our book.

We want to thank David Hirshberg, the executive director of Germaine Lawrence, Inc., for his commitment to and support of this project, and the Ronald McDonald Foundation for providing the funding that made it possible.

We also want to thank our colleagues at Germaine Lawrence as well as our friends and husbands. They read and commented on early drafts, helped with word processing, and gave sustaining support and encouragement. Their faith in us and their enthusiasm for the book were invaluable.

Most importantly, we give our heartfelt thanks to all the girls we have worked with at the Germaine Lawrence School. It was through their ability to share their experiences that we developed our understanding of the impact of sexual abuse on adolescents. Their plight, their courage in dealing with it, and their hope are what stirred us to conceive of this project and fueled our commitment to complete it.

We are especially grateful to the girls who shared their writing and poetry in this workbook in hopes that their words might be helpful to other teenagers: Beth, Ja, Jaime, Jessica, Julie, Renee, and Teresa.

Introduction
How To Use This Workbook

There are 10 chapters in this workbook. Each chapter begins by giving you information about a topic or issue related to sexual abuse. Then there are questions to answer in order to decide what this information has to do with you. We generally review what other teenagers have told us about the topic, frequently using their own words. At the end of each chapter is a section called Suggested Activities. We suggest additional writing, art, reading, and discussion activities that you can do to learn more about the chapter's topic.

Take a Break: Check In with Yourself

In each chapter there will be times when you are instructed to Take a Break: Check In With Yourself. We believe that sometimes you may find the information we provide disturbing. It may make you think about something that has happened to you or bring up hard to manage feelings. Part of your understanding more about your own sexual abuse requires paying attention to what you are thinking and feeling. That's why we ask you to take a break. At these points in each chapter we want you to observe your own thoughts and feelings and then write down what you are thinking and feeling as you do the workbook. This may be confusing. You may find that you need some practice identifying your thoughts and feelings at different times and in different situations. On page x of this book is a Feelings List which you may find helpful if you have trouble coming up with words for your feelings.

Time and Patience

There are many different ways that girls will approach using this workbook. Maybe using this workbook is mostly your therapist's idea, and you think that it's stupid, and that you don't need to talk about this stuff anyway. Or maybe you have decided that you really want to understand your sexual abuse, and that the faster you complete this workbook, the faster you can get thinking about the sexual abuse over with and go on with your life.

Learning about sexual abuse and understanding your own experiences will require time and patience with yourself. Each girl will need to use this workbook in her own time and in her own way. We recommend that you discuss your feelings about using this workbook with your therapist, and that you come up with a plan about how you will use it together. If you are not sure that you think this is a great idea, you might agree to spend 15 minutes of each therapy session on the workbook, or to read and complete a few pages each week. If you are feeling in a hurry to complete this workbook, you might agree to do a chapter a week. It is very likely that there will be times when you want to use this workbook and times when you want to take a break. We recommend that you share these thoughts and feelings with your therapist, and that together you decide on goals for learning about sexual abuse and using this workbook.

Goal-Setting

We believe that therapy will be most helpful if you are able to set your own therapy goals and to decide what you want to achieve by talking about sexual abuse and working in this workbook. In beginning the workbook, you may not be sure what your goals are about your sexual abuse. To start out, your goal may simply be to use the workbook for the amount of time that you and your therapist have agreed upon. When you set a goal or make an agreement with your therapist, we recommend that you write it down so that you both can measure your progress. We have provided a workbook contract form for you and your therapist to record your goals.

As you use this workbook and learn more about sexual abuse, you may decide on other goals that you have in regard to your sexual abuse. We suggest that you and your therapist review your contract regularly, and plan together to help you reach your goals.

We hope that you will give this workbook and your therapist a chance. We know that it is never easy thinking, reading, or talking about sexual abuse. So we understand if you're not feeling enthusiastic about it. We also wish that we could tell you that doing this workbook will make life feel easier or better for you right away, or that once you've completed this workbook, the abuse won't hurt you anymore. We can't do that.

In the beginning, when you first start talking about your sexual abuse, things can almost feel worse, because you may be thinking, feeling, or remembering more about the abuse. But here's the good news. The teenagers with whom we have worked tell us that although the hurt doesn't completely go away, as they have come to understand and talk about the sexual abuse, they feel more positive and in control of their lives.

Workbook Contract

We _____ (teen's name) and _____ (therapist's name) agree that we want to use individual therapy as a place to learn about and talk about sexual abuse.

We have agreed to use this workbook in our therapy sessions for the next _____ weeks. _____ (teen's name) will use the workbook at _____ (place/home, therapist's office, other) and spend _____ minutes using the workbook and/or discussing the workbook in therapy.

_____ (teen's name) has set the following goals for therapy:

1. _____

2. _____

3. _____

4. _____

5. _____

We will review this contract and evaluate the helpfulness of this plan on _____ (date).

_____

(teen's signature)

_____

(therapist's signature)

Feelings List

Accepted	Disrespectful	Paralyzed
Affectionate	Distant	Peaceful
Afraid	Distrustful	Protective
Angry	Embarrassed	Proud
Ashamed	Envious	Rejected
Betrayed	Excited	Relaxed
Calm	Guilty	Relieved
Carefree	Happy	Respectful
Close	Hopeful	Sad
Confident	Hurt	Safe
Confused	Jealous	Sorry
Contented	Lonely	Special
Dependent	Lost	Thankful
Devastated	Loving	Trusting
Disappointed	Neglected	Uncomfortable
Disgusted	Nervous	Worried

I. What Is Sexual Abuse?

"Sexual abuse is when something happens to you sexually that you *do not* want. Many times it includes violence and threats. It's when you feel uncomfortable about how someone is touching you but you feel you can't stop it."

"Sexual abuse is when someone touches you in a sexual way that is against your will, or manipulative, or when you are too young to know it is wrong."

How Do You Define Sexual Abuse?

Has another person ever touched you in a sexual way when you didn't want them to or you felt that you couldn't make them stop? Has an adult ever touched you in a way that made you feel uncomfortable or confused, but you weren't sure if it would be considered sexual abuse?

Teenagers are often uncertain about whether or not a sexual experience that they have had would be defined as sexual abuse. When we begin talking to girls about sexual abuse in therapy we ask them to write their own definitions of sexual abuse. We have included some of their definitions at the beginning of this chapter. The way in which a person defines sexual abuse often has to do with her own experiences and what sexual abuse means to her. Defining sexual abuse is the first step in trying to understand what may have been confusing experiences.

➤ *In the space below, write your own definition of sexual abuse.*

_____

_____

_____

_____

_____

In this workbook, when we talk about sexual abuse we are using the following definitions:

Sexual abuse is any sexual contact or attempt at sexual contact with a child by an adult.

and

Sexual abuse is any use of physical force, threats, bribes, or a position of authority by one person over another person for the purpose of having sexual contact. Whenever a person uses the fact that they are stronger, bigger, or older to have sexual contact with another person, that is sexual abuse.

What Is Sexual Contact?

In the definitions of sexual abuse we mention *sexual contact*. Sexual contact includes all the different ways in which a person can sexually touch or be touched by another person. By sexual contact we mean any of the following:

Kissing: A slow or tongue kiss.

Touching "private parts": Touching the breast, penis, vagina, or buttocks.

Masturbating: Touching one's own or someone else's private parts for sexual pleasure.

Oral sex: Placing the mouth or tongue on a person's vagina or penis.

Finger penetration: Placing a finger in the vagina or buttocks opening.

Intercourse: Placing a penis inside the vaginal opening.

Anal intercourse: Placing a penis inside the buttocks opening.

Dry intercourse (frottage): Rubbing a penis against another person's body.

Child sexual abuse often includes or begins with less obvious sexual contact than we have described above. The person who abuses the child may act as if it is accidental or part of playing a game. He or she may touch the child's private parts while tickling or wrestling. He may make up a game to play with the child that involves undressing or touching each other's bodies or watching someone touch their own or someone else's private parts. It can be very confusing for a child when what starts out as fun and playful turns into sexual touch. Most children would not understand that this type of touching is sexual abuse.

We know that it can be difficult to read about sexual contact. This is a good time to pause.

Take a Break: Check In with Yourself

➤ *What are you thinking after reading this section on sexual contact?*

_____

_____

_____

_____

_____

What Is Inappropriate Sexual Behavior?

Sometimes child sexual abuse begins with or includes inappropriate sexual behavior that does not involve sexual contact but is still abusive to the child. Inappropriate behavior is behavior that is wrong, unacceptable, or hurtful. We have listed some inappropriate behaviors that may be part of sexual abuse.

- Making sexual comments, like talking about a child's private parts in a teasing way
- Ignoring the child's privacy when she is dressing, bathing, or going to the bathroom
- Showing the child photographs or magazine pictures of naked people

- Showing the child movies in which people are having sexual contact
- Taking pictures of the child when she is undressed or asking her to pose for pictures and "act sexy"

Defining inappropriate sexual behavior can be difficult and confusing. When children are young they need help to dress, bathe, and use the toilet. In a large family with only one bathroom it is difficult to maintain privacy at any age. Many movies and TV programs show people having sex, and a lot of popular magazines use models who are not fully clothed. Parents often enjoy photographing their children in a variety of poses and situations. None of these things is necessarily inappropriate or means that a child is being sexually abused. You often need to talk about and describe a situation to figure out if it was part of a pattern of sexual abuse. For instance, there is a difference between being in the room when people are watching a TV movie that has sex scenes and being told to watch an X-rated movie.

No wonder teenagers are often uncertain about whether or not a sexual experience they have had would be defined as sexual abuse. If you are feeling confused, it is important to talk to your therapist. If you are uncomfortable describing something that happened to you, you can still ask questions or give examples of the kinds of situations that confuse you.

➤ *Can you give an example of a situation you're not sure about that might be defined as sexual abuse or sexually inappropriate behavior?*

_____

_____

_____

_____

_____

_____

Who Sexually Abuses Children?

When children or teenagers have been sexually abused, it is often difficult for them to talk about the person who abused them. Sometimes the person who abused them is a stranger. Sometimes the person is someone the child depended on, trusted, or liked. Sometimes the person is a family member. Researchers have found that in about 85% of all cases of child sexual abuse, children knew the people who abused them.

Sexual abuse by a family member is called *incest*. Incest can involve sexual abuse by a mother, father, grandfather, grandmother, uncle, aunt, sister, brother, cousin, brother-in-law, sister-in-law, stepparent, stepsibling, or adoptive parent. We frequently work with girls who have been abused by more than one person. Sometimes they have been abused by people both within and outside of their family.

Some of the words used to name people who sexually abuse children or teenagers are *sexual offender*, *perpetrator*, and *abuser*. In this workbook we call the person who sexually abuses someone the *abuser*.

You Are Not Alone

Teenagers who have been sexually abused often say that they feel weird, strange, or different from other kids. We want you to know that as a teenager who has been sexually abused, you are not alone. It is difficult to know for sure how many people have been sexually abused. However, some research studies show that as many as one out of three girls and one out of six boys have had an experience of sexual abuse before the age of 18.

There are frequent reports of child sexual abuse on television, in newspapers, and in magazines. In recent years a number of celebrities have come forward to tell about the abuse they experienced as children and teenagers. Janet Jackson, a popular rock singer; Oprah Winfrey, an actress and talk show host; Roseanne Arnold, a comedienne; and Marilyn Van Derbur, Miss America 1958, are among the women who have publicly told of their experience with sexual abuse. These women expressed the hope that by sharing their stories they would help other people who have been sexually abused to feel less isolated and alone.

As you continue to use this workbook, you will read things that other teenage girls have written. These girls have also said that by sharing their thoughts, feelings, and experiences about sexual abuse they hope to help other teenagers feel less alone.

In Their Own Words

These definitions of sexual abuse were written by teenage girls.

> "When someone touches you in a place that makes you feel uncomfortable, and when you don't want them to or you don't know that what is being done to you is wrong, and the person doing it to you does know that it's wrong, that's sexual abuse. Also when someone makes you do something you don't want to do to them."

> "I think that sexual abuse is when somebody touches a younger person or a person of the same age sexually, and that person didn't want them to."

> "Sexual abuse is being violated sexually—being sexually taken advantage of—and being exposed to sexuality at an early age."

> "Sexual abuse is when someone forces you to have intercourse, anal sex, oral sex, or any kind of penetration without your permission."

> "Sexual abuse is abusing someone sexually, hurting someone in a sexual way. It doesn't even have to be intercourse, but it could be. It's some sort of touching or making someone just feel uncomfortable."

> "I think it's sexual abuse when someone shows his or her body parts without your wanting to see them or makes you watch sex between a woman and a guy."

> "Sexual abuse is when someone that you trust forces you to have sex unwillingly and threatens you if you say anything."

> "Sexual abuse is when someone violates your body; when without your permission, you are touched in ways you don't want to be touched. It happens whenever you are forced to do sexual things that make you feel bad."

Suggested Activities

- Discuss your goals for therapy with your therapist, then fill in your first Workbook Contract.
- Make a collage about sexual abuse. Cut out pictures or words from magazines and/or newspapers that help to define sexual abuse for you. Then glue them on a piece of construction paper.
- Decorate a folder in which you can keep your writing or pictures about sexual abuse, or
- Buy a notebook or sketchpad for writing and drawing about the sexual abuse, then
- Decide with your therapist where you will keep your writing and artwork about the abuse.

II. The Effects of Sexual Abuse

"Why can't I just put the sexual abuse behind me? What's past is past. I don't see any use in talking about it. I just want to go on with my life."

If you are a teenager who has been sexually abused, it's understandable if you'd like to forget about the abuse. You, too, want to get on with your life in the present and plan for the future. Remembering and thinking about the sexual abuse is difficult and painful. Of course you wish you could make it go away. The problem is that the sexual abuse may be affecting you in the present and getting in the way of your plans for the future. Often the effects of sexual abuse continue to be experienced long after the actual abuse has ended. It can affect the way you think about yourself, your feelings, your behavior, and your relationships with other people.

➤ *How do you think the sexual abuse is affecting you right now?*

_____

_____

_____

_____

_____

_____

Sexual Abuse Is a Trauma

➤ *Look up the word* trauma *in the dictionary. Write the definition below.*
Trauma: _____

_____

_____

_____

_____

_____

➤ *In what ways do you think that sexual abuse is a trauma?*

_____

_____

_____

_____

_____

_____

A trauma is a painful emotional or physical experience that continues to affect and hurt a person even when it is no longer happening. Trauma involves something happening to a person that they cannot stop or control. Natural disasters like floods and hurricanes, car accidents, and living through a war or combat are often experienced as traumas. Sexual abuse is also a trauma. Sexual abuse is a painful emotional or physical experience that continues to affect a person after the abuse ends.

What Is Post-Traumatic Stress Disorder?

Psychologists try to understand how and why certain experiences affect people's thoughts, feelings, and behavior. They have found that different types of traumas (like living through a war, combat, natural disasters, and sexual abuse) seem to affect people in some of the same ways. They have come up with the name *post-traumatic stress disorder* as a way of describing the usual ways in which people are affected by trauma.

Psychologists have also found that people are affected by a trauma after it has happened in two main ways. One way is that they are reminded of the trauma when they don't want to be. We call that *having unwanted reminders*. The other way they are affected by the trauma is that they put a lot of energy into trying to forget that it ever happened. We call that simply *trying to forget*.

➤ *Listed below are some ways people experience unwanted reminders of a trauma like sexual abuse. Check off any of the unwanted reminders that you have experienced.*

☐ Thinking about or remembering the abuse when you're trying to do something else

☐ Having nightmares of the abuse

☐ Feeling like you're reliving or experiencing the abuse in the present—having flashbacks

☐ Feeling upset after seeing, smelling, hearing, or thinking about something that reminds you of the abuse

☐ Thinking or feeling like you've seen the person who abused you even though you know you probably haven't

➤ *Listed below are ways in which people try to forget traumas like sexual abuse. Check off any of the experiences you have had when you're trying to forget.*

☐ Trying to stay away from places, activities, or situations that remind you of the abuse

☐ Trying to push away thoughts or feelings that have to do with the abuse

☐ Not being able to remember long periods of time during your childhood

☐ Feeling distant and different from other people

☐ Not having feelings

☐ Thinking that you won't have a long life or a good future

➤ *There are other signs that tell psychologists that a person is experiencing the aftereffects of a trauma, or post-traumatic stress disorder. Check any of the following signs of post-traumatic stress disorder that you are experiencing:*

☐ Having difficulty falling asleep

☐ Having difficulty staying asleep

☐ Having trouble concentrating

☐ Being easily angered

☐ Being overly watchful and alert to danger

☐ Being jumpy when touched or approached unexpectedly

This is a good time to pause.

Take a Break: Check In with Yourself

➤ *What are you thinking?*

_____

_____

_____

_____

_____

_____

_____

_____

➤ *How are you feeling?*

_____

_____

_____

_____

_____

_____

_____

_____

Teenagers and Post-Traumatic Stress Disorder

> "After being sexually abused, I had problems with school, drug abuse, and alcohol abuse. I used drugs and alcohol to cover the mask that was falling apart, and I acted out in school so I would be noticed by people both in school and in my home, because I didn't think I was getting enough attention."

Often teenagers feel like there is no one that they can talk to about being sexually abused. They try to look their best on the outside, to keep up the "mask" and to push away their thoughts and feelings about the abuse. They may try to forget the abuse by doing things that help them to forget. They may act in ways that let people know they need help or attention without telling anyone that they've been sexually abused. Below are some behaviors that may be signs a teenager is experiencing post-traumatic stress disorder as a result of sexual abuse.

➤ *Place a check beside any of these behaviors that you have tried.*

- ☐ Drinking a lot
- ☐ Drug abuse
- ☐ Eating a lot
- ☐ Not eating
- ☐ Having sex a lot with people you hardly know
- ☐ Running away
- ☐ Cutting or scratching yourself
- ☐ Trying to commit suicide

In Their Own Words

We have asked the girls we work with to write about the effects of sexual abuse. Here are some of their thoughts:

> "Sexual abuse leaves a permanent painful mark on your mind and heart."

> "I feel that sexual abuse has many different effects on people. Some people may feel embarrassed by what happened because the persons saw their body naked and made them feel dirty or cheap. For others, it may make them blame themselves for what happened, feeling that it was their fault, they made this happen, or other feelings like this. A very few people feel angry at the person, and for them, if there was anything like love, affection, admirable feelings—if the person was an idol or a role model—these are lost forever."

> "I think sexual abuse affects different people in different ways. But the one thing that stands out in my mind the most is how it affects families. I think it pulls a family apart. I also think it makes a person feel differently about herself or himself. Another thing I think happens is the way someone looks at others, like authority figures, fathers, baby-sitters, and so on."

> "I am still affected by the abuse by being scared of almost everybody. I have a real difficult time trusting anyone. I remember my abuse very frequently like I am really there. My feelings that I carry now are mainly jumbled. My self-worth

is still pretty low. I have a hard time feeling like I deserve anything. I have a difficult time with all the relationships I have developed. I get nervous when people get too close, physically and emotionally. That's why many of my relationships have disappeared. Even with my family, if things are going well I always end up doing something wrong or stupid and ruining it. But I do it unconsciously. My feelings toward sexuality come through in my eating disorder. I don't want to be attractive, I don't want hips, breasts, or a butt. Thinking about sex makes me nauseous."

"Why am I suffering so much now from my past when my past is over? Sometimes I think it's not over. I can't trust anyone. I'm still suffering and I have my pain still with me."

Suggested Activities

- Ask your therapist to look up *traumatic disorders* with you in the book called *Diagnostic and Statistical Manual of Mental Disorders*. Ask your therapist any questions you have about post-traumatic stress disorder.
- Discuss what other experiences besides sexual abuse might cause a person to have the symptoms of post-traumatic stress.
- Describe in detail what your unwanted reminders have been like.
- Write a poem or draw a picture that expresses how your experience of sexual abuse has affected you.
- Write a story about a teenager who was sexually abused when she was a little girl. What is she like now? How has she been affected by the sexual abuse?

III. It Takes Courage to Remember

"Memories are sometimes hard to face. Memories are thinking about the things that happened to me in the past. Some memories are hard to think about. Memories usually stay inside of me for a long, long time.

Talking about memories is very hard. Memories usually make me feel like crying. Memories are hard when I don't know what to do."

Remembering that you have been sexually abused can be difficult, and scary. Webster's Dictionary defines courage as "facing and dealing with anything recognized as dangerous, difficult, or painful instead of withdrawing from it." It takes courage to face and deal with your memories of sexual abuse.

In the last chapter you learned about post-traumatic stress disorder. You looked at the ways in which you experience unwanted reminders of the abuse and the ways in which you try to forget that you have been sexually abused. Experiencing unwanted reminders of sexual abuse, like nightmares and flashbacks, can leave you feeling confused and out of control. You may even wonder, "Am I going crazy?" There may be times when it is difficult for you to trust your memories and to believe that the abuse really happened. At times remembering the abuse can be overwhelming, because along with the memories come upsetting feelings like anger, sadness, and fear. You may also be worried about unexpectedly getting more new memories.

It can be very frustrating if you think that you can't remember some of the times you were sexually abused. You may not be doing anything to try to forget the abuse, but you still can't get back the memories. It can be very troubling to feel like you can't control how much you remember or the ways in which you get memories or unwanted reminders of the abuse.

➤ *How much of your sexual abuse do you think you remember? Place a check beside the statement that is most like your situation. If none of these statements fits for you, please write your own description under Other.*

☐ I have some memories of the abuse. They seem unclear and like puzzle pieces that don't fit together.

☐ I remember some parts of the abuse clearly; other memories are fuzzy and confusing.

☐ I remember most of the details of the abuse clearly.

13

☐ I don't have any clear memories of the sexual abuse. I think that I was abused because:

   ☐ the abuser admitted to it.

   ☐ another adult said that it happened.

   ☐ I told someone about it when I was much younger.

☐ Other _____

➤ *In which of these ways do you experience memories of the abuse?*

   ☐ In dreams

   ☐ In thoughts

   ☐ In pictures or images in your mind

   ☐ By hearing voices in your head

   ☐ By having flashbacks and reliving the abuse in your mind or body

➤ *Describe below what it is like for you to remember the abuse.*

_____

_____

_____

_____

_____

_____

_____

_____

What Triggers Your Memories?

Some girls have told us that they feel like they are having memories of the sexual abuse all the time. Others have said that they never know where or when they will have an upsetting memory. However, if you begin to pay close attention, you may find that most of your memories are triggered by particular times, places, or situations. Any one of our five senses—sight, sound, smell, taste, or touch—can set off a memory from the past. The things that trigger your memory of the abuse are usually in some way related to the abuse. If you can identify and understand what triggers your memories, you may feel less frightened or overwhelmed by remembering the abuse. In the exercises below, you are asked to think about what times, places, people, or events trigger your memories of the sexual abuse.

If you are having difficulty remembering the abuse, when you do these exercises think about times, places, and situations that are upsetting to you. Ask yourself if your feelings are in any way connected to the abuse.

Exercise 1: When?

➤ *Try to think about the time of day, day of the week, or time of the year when you are most likely to remember the abuse. Do you think about the abuse when you wake up, during a particular class, or at bedtime? Do you think about the abuse more on weekends or weekdays? Is there a particular season of the year or holiday when you have strong memories of the abuse?*

_____

_____

_____

_____

_____

_____

_____

_____

_____

_____

_____

_____

_____

_____

_____

_____

_____

_____

_____

_____

_____

_____

_____

_____

_____

_____

_____

_____

_____

_____

Exercise 2: Where?

➤ *Do particular places bring back memories of the sexual abuse? Is there a room in your house where you're most likely to have memories: bedroom, living room, kitchen, basement? Are there outdoor areas that trigger memories, such as playgrounds, swimming pools, woods, schoolyards? What places do you connect with remembering the abuse?*

_____

_____

_____

_____

_____

_____

_____

_____

_____

_____

_____

_____

_____

_____

_____

_____

_____

_____

_____

_____

_____

_____

_____

_____

_____

_____

Exercise 3: What or Who?

➤ *Below are some situations that trigger memories of sexual abuse for other teenagers. Check off any experience that also triggers memories for you.*

☐ Seeing the abuser

☐ Seeing a person who looks like the abuser

☐ Looking at a drawing of the human body in science class

☐ Being in sex education classes; seeing sex education textbooks or movies

☐ Hearing running water in the bathtub or shower

☐ Smelling a particular food cooking

☐ Eating a particular food

☐ Eating in general

☐ Being hugged by a woman

☐ Being hugged by a man

☐ Being touched by a woman

☐ Being touched by a man

☐ Smelling cologne or perfume

➤ *List the situations that are most likely to trigger memories of the sexual abuse for you.*

1. _____
2. _____
3. _____
4. _____
5. _____

➤ *Do you think that there are people, places, or situations that you stay away from because you think you might be reminded of the sexual abuse? If yes, what are they?*

1. _____
2. _____
3. _____
4. _____
5. _____

Once you are able to identify situations that trigger your memories, you have some choices about how to handle remembering the abuse. Planning and exercising the choices that you do have can make you feel in control. In the next chapter we will discuss how to develop plans that can help you cope with your memories.

Take a Break: Check In with Yourself

➤ *What are you thinking after completing this chapter?*

_____

_____

_____

_____

_____

➤ *How are you feeling?*

_____

_____

_____

_____

In Their Own Words

Remembering

"Sometimes remembering can be hard. It is often trying and difficult. It seems as though you try so hard to remember the bad things that it makes you forget some of the good. The first memory was hard for me. I always had ideas of what had happened but I never had all the facts. And when I remembered the first memory all the others seemed to rise to the surface shortly after. But along with the memories come feelings of guilt, anger, and fear. And you start putting your feelings with the actions of the past. For me it made my memories clearer and more exact. Every once in a while I get another memory. I no longer push it down as I did in the past. I just sit down and let it finish informing me. It doesn't get easier remembering that I was abused. The hurt is always there. It's just easier to deal with it and live with it."

Memories

"I was such an innocent little girl with long brown pigtails and blue eyes. I didn't have a care in the world, until I was four. Then the nightmare began. I remember being scared to go to his house, but I did because I wanted to see my aunt. I loved my aunt. She was always nice to me. She didn't do anything wrong. She was just blind to the possibility of my abuse, like everyone else. He was nice, too. But in a bad way. He used to touch me in ways that I didn't like. He made me do things to him that I didn't like. He made me the center of everyone's attention, which disgraced me and my family, and I hate him. I hate him for the memories of my childhood that he left me—cold, bitter, and stinging memories."

Suggested Activities

- Write down one memory, dream, or flashback about the abuse. Write down another.
- Draw a picture of the place where you remember being abused.
- Write about "Why I don't want to believe my memories."
- If you have flashbacks, describe in as much detail as you can when they come and what they are like.
- Explain why you think that particular times, places, or situations trigger memories of the abuse for you.
- Make a collage about memories of abuse.

IV. Coping with Your Memories

"Grounding means anything that someone who has been sexually abused can do to cope when they are feeling frightened by flashbacks or remembering the abuse. It includes a number of things you can do to feel safe and comforted and get connected to the present ground."

Grounding

When you are having a memory or an unwanted reminder of the sexual abuse, there are some things that you can do to feel grounded. We have listed some steps that have helped others to feel safe and in control while they are experiencing difficult memories. They can help you to feel better.

1. Take deep breaths. Try counting each time that you breathe out.
2. Tap your feet on the ground. If you are sitting in a chair hold on to the arms or the seat of the chair.
3. Look around. Remind yourself of where you are right now.
4. Tell yourself, "I am safe now. I am OK. I am having a memory of something that happened in the past."
5. Hold on to something safe and comforting, like a stuffed animal or other special object.

After the memory passes, you may decide to immediately write down what you remember in a journal so you don't forget. Or it may be better for you to do something active that takes your mind off remembering. In therapy, you can talk about and plan what will be most helpful to you.

You can also plan ahead when you know that some time or place triggers your memories. For instance, if you know that bedtime is a difficult time for you, you can plan comforting and relaxing things to do at night that make bedtime easier. The girls who we work with have told us that some of the following activities help them feel grounded: drawing, reading, journal writing, listening to music or taped stories, playing a game, and drinking herbal tea. Use whatever helps you to feel grounded or comforted and relaxed. On page xx is a grounding plan that you can work on with your therapist. We hope that it will help you to feel safe and in control of your memories.

Flooding and Freezing

In the last chapter we discussed the different ways in which people experience memories of sexual abuse. It is important to understand that each person remembers in her own way and in her own time. Some of you may feel like you are remembering too much, too fast. Others may feel like you are remembering too little, too slowly. Perhaps you go back and forth between being overwhelmed by memories too much of the time, or *flooding*, and then trying to avoid thinking of the abuse by numbing your thoughts and feelings, or *freezing*.

➤ *How do you cope with your memories of the sexual abuse?*

☐ Flooding: Thinking about it too much; feeling overwhelmed

☐ Freezing: Trying not to think about it; numbing

☐ Flooding and freezing: Going back and forth between the two

You can increase your control over remembering the abuse by paying attention to how you are coping with your memories. If you are a person who is most likely to flood, it is important for you to learn to contain your memories so they don't interfere too much with your daily life. If you are a person who freezes, you will need to learn to gradually let yourself express thoughts and feelings about the sexual abuse.

How are you coping right now? Are your memories increasing and interfering with your daily life? Are you flooding, and having difficulty putting away your thoughts and feelings about the abuse? Or are you freezing, putting a lot of energy into avoiding your memories?

➤ *A barometer is an instrument for measuring the pressure changes in the atmosphere that predict changes in the weather. You can use your own barometer to measure the pressure you are experiencing as a result of remembering or trying not to remember the abuse. You can use this picture of a barometer to measure how you are being affected by remembering. On one end is freezing, on the other end is flood warning, and all the other weather conditions are in between.*

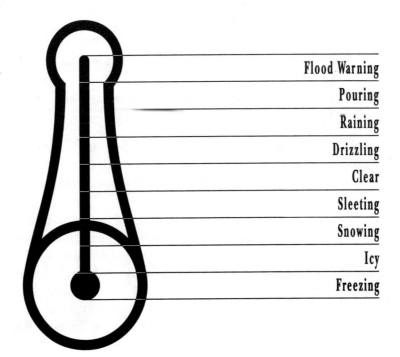

Flood Warning

Pouring

Raining

Drizzling

Clear

Sleeting

Snowing

Icy

Freezing

Where Are You on the Barometer Right Now?

Flood Warning

If you are above *raining* on the barometer, either *pouring* or *flooding,* you could use a special plan to help you deal with the pressure of increased memories. You need to find ways to slow down and contain the abuse work so that you can feel better and safer. This process will help you to identify and understand what is triggering your memories of the abuse. Then you can plan the times and ways in which you will deal with your memories. You can also plan things to do to make yourself feel better and to stop thinking so much about the abuse, using the Flood Warning Action Plan on page xx.

Freezing Conditions

It is possible that being flooded with memories has not been a problem for you. Maybe you find that when you remember the abuse you feel numb. You don't think you have any feelings about the abuse. As a matter of fact, you're not sure you have many feelings about anything in your life. Sometimes people discover that having numbed themselves to the pain of experiencing and remembering the sexual abuse has left them numb and distant from other life experiences, "frozen" inside. Some of you may feel like you are experiencing freezing conditions most of the time.

Now that you are in therapy and using this workbook, you may have decided that you want that to change. Perhaps you want to begin to piece together more of your memories, and to connect your feelings to your memories. We understand that this kind of change can be very scary. If you are below Snowing on the barometer, the Freezing Conditions Action Plan (see page xx) can help you to feel more aware and in control of remembering the abuse. It will help you to identify what triggers your sexual abuse memories and to begin to connect feelings to your memories.

Sometimes people go back and forth between being flooded with painful memories and trying to deal with the pain by numbing and freezing. If you go back and forth between flooding and freezing, using the barometer and the action plans should help you to find the middle and feel clear.

Take a Vacation Break

It is also important that you try to regularly take a break from thinking about the sexual abuse. You can work so hard at remembering and dealing with sexual abuse that you forget to be a teenager. You need and deserve to have fun with other people, go places and do things that you enjoy, and let yourself relax. We all need to take vacation breaks and go somewhere warm and sunny, at least in our minds. The Vacation Break form on page xx will help you to identify things you can do when you need a vacation. If you feel it's impossible to get to a warm and sunny place in yourself right now, settle for partly cloudy. Vacation breaks are too important for you to ignore!

Grounding Plan

➤ *These times, places, or situations trigger my memories of the sexual abuse:*

_____

_____

_____

_____

_____

➤ *When I have an upsetting memory, I can ground myself by:*

1. _____

2. _____

3. _____

➤ *After the memory passes, I can do the following things to feel safe and grounded:*

1. _____

2. _____

3. _____

➤ *I can plan ahead to deal with times that are particularly difficult for me, like _____ (time). I can do the following things to help myself feel grounded at this time:*

1. _____

2. _____

3. _____

Flood Warning Action Plan

➤ *On the barometer I rated myself as (circle one):*

Flood Warning	Pouring	Raining	Drizzling
Clear	Sleeting	Snowing	Icy	Frozen

➤ *I started flooding when:*

_____

_____

_____

_____

_____

➤ *I was reminded of my abuse by:*

_____

_____

_____

_____

_____

_____

➤ *I want to continue working on remembering my abuse. At the same time, right now I need to slow down and feel safe. To slow down on my abuse work I will:*

_____

_____

_____

_____

_____

_____

➤ *To help myself feel better, safer, and more relaxed I will:*

1. _____

2. _____

3. _____

4. _____

Freezing Conditions Action Plan

➤ *On the barometer I rated myself as (circle one):*

Flood Warning	Pouring	Raining	Drizzling
Clear	Sleeting	Snowing	Icy	Frozen

➤ *I started feeling this way when:*

_____

_____

_____

_____

_____

_____

➤ *I wanted to stop thinking about the abuse after:*

_____

_____

_____

_____

_____

➤ *I need to take a break from working on remembering my abuse. The break will help me to:*

_____

_____

_____

_____

_____

➤ *I will slowly try to start working on the abuse again. I will do this by:*

1. _____
2. _____
3. _____
4. _____

Vacation Break Plan

➤ *I have been working very hard on remembering and understanding my sexual abuse. Thinking about my abuse so much is making it difficult for me to feel like a normal person and do things I need to do, such as:*

_____

_____

_____

_____

_____

➤ *I am going to take a vacation break from my sexual abuse work from _____ (date) to _____ (date). I need to do things that make me feel better about myself. Favorite activities that I can plan to do over my vacation are:*

1. _____
2. _____
3. _____
4. _____

➤ *If I am having a lot of memories, I can ground myself by:*

1. _____
2. _____
3. _____
4. _____

In Their Own Words

This poem suggests some things you can do to help yourself get through the hard days.

Help Yourself

If you're down,
Just look around.
Look in the sky:
There's a bird that can fly!
Or when you feel low
Look out your window,
See the rain
Trickle out your pain.
If you get depressed,
Maybe get dressed;
What you wear
Can help you face fear.
When things get confusing,
Do something amusing,
Like stand on your head
Or jump on your bed.
There's many ways
To get through hard days.
Whether you're a girl or boy,
Just find what you enjoy.

Suggested Activities

- Make a poster about grounding to remind yourself how to deal with difficult memories.
- Make a collage of activities that you enjoy.
- Describe a place where you feel safe and relaxed, or draw a picture of it.
- Make a list of music that will help you to feel better if you are sad or lonely.
- Review your Workbook Contract with your therapist and decide whether you want to change any of your therapy goals.

V. Keeping the Secret

When you are a little girl, it is very difficult to keep a secret. If you know about a present that someone is getting for her birthday or a surprise event being planned, it is really hard not to tell. When you are little, trying to keep a secret usually makes you excited or silly. Even when you don't tell the secret you may let somebody know that you've got a secret to tell.

Yet researchers have found that children who are being sexually abused often don't tell anyone. What is it about sexual abuse that causes a child to keep it secret? What is it about sexual abuse that causes a child to suffer silently?

Are you still keeping some part of your sexual abuse a secret? Even though you have told your therapist that you were abused, you may have kept the name of the abuser or the details of the abuse secret. Sometimes, when children have been sexually abused by more than one person, they have told about one situation of sexual abuse, but they have never spoken about the other abuse that they experienced. Since you are now a teenager you may have been suffering silently for a long time.

Why Does a Child Keep Sexual Abuse a Secret?

In order for child sexual abuse to occur, the abuser, in most situations, must somehow get a child alone and then convince the child to keep the abuse a secret. In the first chapter we defined sexual abuse as any use of physical force, threats, bribes, or a position of authority by one person over another person for the purpose of having sexual contact.

Listed below are some of the things abusers have said or done to get a child to keep the secret of sexual abuse.

➤ *Check off any of the things on this list that the abuser said or did to you.*

☐ Said "No one will believe you if you tell."

☐ Said "People will blame you if you tell."

☐ Said "Your mother will leave me if you tell."

☐ Said "Your mother will be mad at you if you tell."

☐ Said "I will go to prison."

☐ Said "They will take you away."

- ☐ Said "I won't love you."
- ☐ Said "The family will break apart if you tell."
- ☐ Said "You liked it—you came on to me."
- ☐ Threatened to hurt a person you care about.
- ☐ Threatened to hurt a pet.
- ☐ Threatened to hurt you.
- ☐ Threatened to kill you.
- ☐ Made you feel special.
- ☐ Made you feel like you were the only one who cared and understood him or her.
- ☐ Made you feel pretty.
- ☐ Made you feel dirty and bad.
- ☐ Gave you money.
- ☐ Gave you presents.
- ☐ Gave you special privileges.
- ☐ Gave you attention.

Sometimes the abuser doesn't say or do anything in particular to get the child to keep the secret. The abuser doesn't have to: he or she is older, bigger, stronger, and more powerful than the child. If the abuser is a grownup and the child has been taught to obey adults, the child will simply do as the adult wishes. If the abuser is a family member, then the child may believe that he or she will love and protect the child. In the beginning the child may not understand that what the abuser is doing is bad or wrong. She may think, "If an adult or a family member is doing this to me, it must be OK." But that doesn't mean she isn't scared and confused by the experience of the abuse.

The abuser often finds silent ways to tell the child to keep the abuse a secret. The abuse often happens in secrecy when the child and the abuser are alone. During the abuse the abuser may act very differently toward the child than he or she does at other times. This secrecy makes it clear to the child that something bad and dangerous is happening, even if the abuser doesn't say a word. If you are a teenager who was sexually abused as a child, it may still be difficult for you to tell the secret. If you are a teenager who was sexually abused as a child, then that scared, confused, and threatened child still lives within you.

➤ *What did the person who abused you do that caused you to keep the secret?*

_____

_____

_____

_____

_____

_____

Take a Break: Check In with Yourself

➤ *What are you thinking after reading this section on keeping the secret?*

_____

_____

_____

_____

_____

➤ *How are you feeling?*

_____

_____

_____

Living with the Secret

"I feel like everyone would hate me if I told them anything about my past, and I would feel really hurt if anyone hated me because of it."

Living with the secret of sexual abuse can make you feel lonely, different, and distant from other people. Even if you do have friends and get along well with some of the adults in your life, you may be thinking, "But they don't know the real me." Teenagers we have known said that if their friends knew they were sexually abused, they "would think I'm weird," "would make fun of me," or "wouldn't want to be my friend." Living with the secret of sexual abuse makes it difficult to trust people, get close to people, or let anyone know the real you.

When children or teenagers have been sexually abused, instead of saying to themselves "something bad has happened to me," they often say "I am bad." They do not realize that their sexual abuse was a trauma, an overwhelming and painful experience that they could not stop or control. They blame themselves for the abuse. Living with the secret of sexual abuse makes it impossible to clear up these confusing thoughts and feelings by sharing them with another person.

➤ *How have you been affected by keeping the secret of sexual abuse? How has it affected your relationships with other people?*

_____

_____

_____

_____

If you have been living with the secret of sexual abuse, then you have been putting a lot of effort into keeping the secret. Maybe you have had to lie, cover up, or pretend so that no one would find out the truth. You have believed that you needed the secret in order to be safe and to protect other people.

➤ *Who have you protected by keeping the sexual abuse a secret?*

_____

_____

_____

_____

_____

➤ *What have you feared will happen if you tell the secret?*

_____

_____

_____

_____

_____

Now that you are in therapy and using this workbook, you don't have to be all alone with your thoughts and feelings about the abuse. Therapy provides a safe place where you can choose to gradually talk about the abuse. Your therapist can help you to evaluate whether you want to share secrets you are still keeping, either in therapy or with other people in your life. You have taken a major step in breaking the silence. You don't have to live your life in secrecy.

In Their Own Words

These two journal entries describe what kept one child from breaking the silence.

> "Tonight I was thinking about school. All I could think of was when I was in school and how I kept getting held back. I didn't realize what was happening or why I was getting held back. Then I realized that it was not me, it was because I couldn't trust anyone and I was getting sexually abused and beaten at home. I can remember when my teacher used to pull me aside and say, "What's going on with you? Talk to me." I remember that and I wish now I could have told her, but there were too many things happening to me, and anyway I don't think I could have told her. I couldn't trust anyone anyway—parents, relatives, guys, strangers, cops—nobody! There wasn't anyone I could turn to. Now I'm trying to get help from other people, but it's so hard for me. Sometimes it's hard for me to explain how I'm feeling. I know that I can do it, but I need help. I can't be doing it by myself."

"When I was a little girl I was scared about everything that was around me. I couldn't trust people or even feel for them. I didn't know the things that were happening to me were bad and wrong. I felt so scared to trust people. I thought that if I did I was going to get raped or sexually abused. I didn't even feel anything while I was getting sexually abused by so many people. It was like my body was numb or I was going through a shock. I wanted to tell my mother but I thought she might start hitting me. I felt so alone. I didn't trust anyone, so I couldn't turn to anyone for help! I didn't even know if it was bad. My mother never taught me anything about people touching me."

Suggested Activities

- Write a story about a child or teenager who had been abused and kept it a secret for a long time. Talk about why she kept it secret for so long. What stopped her from telling? What finally gave her the courage to break her silence and tell someone?
- Write your thoughts and feelings about keeping the abuse secret in the format of a poem or a song.
- What would you say to a child who is being abused now about keeping a secret?
- Are there good secrets and bad secrets? What's the difference between them?

VI. What Happens When You Tell

Trying to Tell

Children and teenagers who are being sexually abused may try to tell about the abuse in many different ways. Sometimes, before they tell someone directly in words that they are being abused, they will try to tell through their behavior or by dropping hints. They may cry or become fearful, hide, or run away when they have contact with the abuser. They may tell someone that they hate the abuser or that the abuser is bothering or hurting them. Children may act out the abuse when they are playing games, such as house or dolls. Children and teenagers may become withdrawn or get into trouble at home or in school to try to let others know how troubled they are feeling about the abuse.

➤ *Did you ever try to tell about your abuse through hints or through your behavior? In what ways?*

_____

_____

_____

_____

In some situations a child or teenager may know or think that another person knew about the abuse without their telling. They may remember that another person observed or participated in their abuse. Or they may think that someone else knew even though that person didn't see the abuse occur.

➤ *Do you think that anyone knew you were being abused before you told? If you do, what makes you think that they knew?*

_____

_____

_____

_____

Those of you who are using this workbook may be at very different points in telling about your abuse. You may only have told your therapist that you have been abused or you may have told a number of people. Some of you have told very little about the abuse that you experienced. Others have told someone most of the details that they remember. You may have told a lot about one person who abused you and still be keeping other situations in which you were abused a secret.

➤ *Which of the following describes your situation?*

☐ I've told my therapist that I have been abused, but I haven't told the details.

☐ I've told my therapist most of the details about my abuse.

☐ I've told the following people the details of the abuse: _____

_____

_____

☐ I've told some people that I was abused, but I haven't told them the details. I told:

_____

_____

_____

☐ I've never told my therapist about one of the people who abused me.

☐ I've never told anyone about one of the people who abused me.

When a child or teenager first tells someone that they are being sexually abused, they may or may not be believed. Telling one person about the abuse can also result in other people being told. Sexual abuse is against the law, and most states require that professionals like therapists and teachers report to the state's child protection agency when they suspect that a child or teenager has been sexually abused. A person who you told might have reported your abuse to the police or other authorities.

➤ *What was your experience when you told?*

☐ I was believed by the first person that I told.

☐ I was not believed by the first person that I told.

☐ I was believed by _____

_____

☐ But not believed by _____

_____

☐ A person I told reported it to the:

☐ police

☐ child protective services

☐ other _____

What Happened When You Told?

➤ *In the space below tell the story of what happened when you told. How long ago was it when you told? Who did you tell and what was their reaction? What, if anything, happened afterward? What made it possible for you to tell about the abuse at that time?*

_____

_____

_____

_____

_____

_____

_____

_____

_____

_____

_____

_____

_____

_____

_____

_____

_____

_____

_____

_____

_____

_____

_____

_____

_____

_____

_____

_____

_____

_____

_____

Take a Break: Check In with Yourself

➤ *What are you thinking after completing this section of the workbook?*

_____

_____

_____

_____

➤ *How are you feeling?*

_____

_____

_____

_____

The Benefits and Difficulties of Telling

It took courage to tell someone that you have been sexually abused. You had to overcome your fears about telling, and you had no way to predict what would happen after you told. If you had to face a lot of difficulties after you told about the abuse, you may sometimes wish you had never told. Hopefully, you have also experienced benefits from telling. The following exercise was designed to help you evaluate how you have been affected by telling about your abuse.

Exercise: Benefits and Difficulties

➤ *List the benefits and difficulties of telling. Try to imagine how it might have been if you hadn't told.*

Benefits

1. _____

2. _____

3. _____

4. _____

Difficulties

1. _____

2. _____

3. _____

4. _____

When we asked some teenagers to give us their thoughts on the benefits and difficulties of telling, this is what they said:

Benefits of Telling
- The abuser might get taken out of the house.
- You can start to get help with what happened to you.
- You don't get abused anymore.
- Your parents will understand your mood swings or the reason you've been acting strange.
- The person who sexually abused you could get help.
- You don't have to hold all your feelings inside anymore.
- You could leave the house.
- You would find out that you're not alone.
- You would realize that others have shared the same things.

Another teenager gave this list:

- Being believed.
- Getting outside support.
- Admitting what happened.
- Sharing my feelings.
- Realizing that I'm not guilty.
- Relieving the stress.
- Having someone listen.

Difficulties of Telling
- You might not be believed.
- Your family might not support you. They might think it's not important, that it's just a normal part of life.
- You'd be accusing a loved one.
- People would ask you hard questions, ask you to remember, to talk in detail.
- You could have flashbacks.
- If you go to court, that can be hard.
- There may be pressure to continue to talk.
- People may find out and hold it against you.
- It could affect your relationships with people in your family.
- You could be accused of lying.
- The abuser could deny that he or she abused you.
- The abuser might be very angry with you.

Deciding to Tell

If you are trying to decide whether you want to tell more about your abuse in therapy, you probably have mixed feelings. You may also be feeling uncertain if you are questioning whether or not to tell a family member or friend about the abuse. It is likely that you have both hopes and fears about telling. We hope that you will continue to use therapy and this workbook to support you through these decisions. The lists of benefits and difficulties, both the one you made and the one above, may help you with your decision-making.

In Their Own Words

A Relationship

I was young, he was old.

He loved me,

Or so I was told.

I loved him, and still do;

I'm just confused

And have no clue.

Why did he want to do that?

I just don't understand.

If I tell I'll be a rat.

I was hurt and I was scared.

But I was wrong,

And he's the one that dared.

My life is such a mess. I have been having such a bad day today. Today I told people that my mother's boyfriend did touch me. For the first time today, in eight years, I have finally said something. I am so scared to go out, to live my life, and to trust and love people. Why can't I just have a normal family and a normal life? If I told my mother that I am scared (of her boyfriend) she would never see me again and she would give up on me. I want to be with my mother, but I also want him to get some help.

Suggested Activities

- Write about what you wish had happened when you told.
- Discuss what you would do if a friend told you that she or he was being sexually abused. What advice would you give?
- If you are having trouble telling your therapist about the abuse, fill out the form on the benefits and difficulties of telling.
- Discuss with your therapist what she or he can do to make it easier for you to tell.
- Make a collage to express your fears about telling.

VII. Telling The Details

"Why the details? Why do I need to talk about that?! It's sickening. It's too awful to say, too painful. I'll get too embarrassed. If anyone knew that about me they'd think badly of me. There are some things I will never be able to tell anyone."

This is the kind of response we often get when we encourage girls to talk about the details of their abuse in therapy. By talking about the details, we mean talking about how you were abused and when and where the abuse occurred.

We understand that for some girls it is difficult to say the words *sexual abuse* out loud, let alone talk about parts of their body or kinds of sexual contact. In previous chapters we've talked about the painful effects of living with a secret. You've also been exploring the benefits and difficulties you might face if you talk more about the abuse. It takes courage to tell the details of your sexual abuse. Remember that courage means facing something that is painful, difficult, or scary without withdrawing from it.

How Can Telling Help Me?

1. It can relieve you from the stress involved in keeping a secret.

   The longer you hold onto a secret the more draining it becomes. In order to keep a secret you must always be cautious about what you say. There is a part of yourself that must always remain hidden from others. Sometimes you have to lie in order to keep the secret. This makes it difficult to be relaxed or open with people. It may be hard to concentrate in school or at your job, because when you are keeping a secret you must be preoccupied with that task.

2. It can help you to feel more connected to other people.

   Many of the girls we have worked with said that if anyone knew the details of their abuse they would "think badly of me," "reject me," or "hate me." One girl said it was as though the fear and shame about sexual abuse keeps you in a prison. You cannot truly connect with others. You are alone. The details can be so frightening for you that you cannot break free.

Telling the details to a therapist who you trust can help you begin to feel connected to other people. The support and understanding of another person can help you to feel less fearful and to grow more accepting of yourself. If you can begin to tell the details, slowly, at your own pace, you can gradually overcome your fear of them. In time, they will not have so much power over you. They will always be facts about your life, but they may not always make you flinch, cringe, tune out, or act out.

The more comfortable you get in talking about the facts and feelings of your abuse, the less imprisoned you should feel.

3. It can help you to have more control over your memories.

   In the chapter on post-traumatic stress disorder we described how people who have experienced a trauma, such as sexual abuse, often expend a lot of energy trying to forget. However, they often have unwanted reminders of the abuse, memories that come back uninvited and without warning. Unwanted reminders of your abuse can leave you feeling frightened, overwhelmed, and out of control. When you begin talking about the details of your abuse in therapy, you begin to take control over remembering. Over time, talking about the abuse may lessen the frequency of unwanted reminders. As you grow comfortable with talking about the abuse, you may be able to planfully remember more and feel less disrupted when you are reminded of the abuse.

4. It will help you take care of yourself.

   Keeping this secret, holding back your memories keeps you from being the most you can be. You may be spending tremendous amounts of energy on keeping the secret rather than on living your life!

Why should you have to keep a secret about something someone else did? It's something someone else should be ashamed of—not you! Why should you be hindered in any way from excelling in your schoolwork, your job, or your relationships?

Starting to Tell

The following section is made up of writing exercises with questions that can help you to tell the details. We realize that telling the details may be a very difficult and painful process, so we encourage you to answer these questions and do these exercises your way:

- *At your own pace*. You may want to do them all at once or over a long period of time. While you are working on this chapter it may be helpful to plan a Vacation Break.
- *In your own order*. You may want to skip parts or do them in a different order.
- *In the style you like*. These questions are only meant to help you get started. If it suits you better to sit down and write a few journal pages, or a poem, a song, or just bits and pieces about the abuse, then do it.
- *According to what is comfortable for you at this time*. If you can only answer one question, that's fine. If you can answer all of them and have a lot more to say, great! It may feel right to allow weeks or even months for these exercises.

Perhaps you were abused by several people. If you can, do this exercise for each person who abused you.

We congratulate you for beginning this section. We admire your courage and determination.

Exercise 1: Who, What, Where, When?

➤ *Who abused you?*

_____

_____

_____

➤ *How old were you when the abuse started?*

_____

_____

_____

➤ *How old were you when the abuse ended?*

_____

_____

_____

➤ *Where did it usually happen? In what place, what room, where in the room?*

_____

_____

_____

➤ *Were there other people around? Who? Where were they?*

_____

_____

_____

➤ *Did it happen on particular days, on holidays, or on weekends?*

_____

_____

_____

➤ *What time of day or night did it usually happen? Any reason for this particular time of day?*

_____

_____

➤ *Right before it ended, how often was the abuse occurring? How many times a day, week, or month?*

_____

_____

_____

Exercise 2: The Beginning

Often, as teenagers look back, they see that the sexual abuse started before the sexual contact. In the first chapter we listed some of the less obvious ways that sexual abuse may begin. These included the abuser talking or teasing about sexual things, ignoring your privacy, or touching your private parts while wrestling or tickling you.

In this exercise, try to think about the very beginning of the abuse. What might have been the first signs? What was the first time you began feeling uncomfortable? You may be surprised to find that you can see what was happening more clearly now, looking back, than when you were actually experiencing it.

_____

_____

_____

_____

_____

_____

_____

_____

_____

_____

_____

_____

_____

_____

_____

_____

_____

_____

_____

_____

_____

_____

_____

Exercise 3: What Happened

As the abuse continued, the amount of sexual contact may have increased and patterns may have developed. The questions in this exercise are to help you tell the details of what usually happened. Where did the abuser touch you? With what part of their body?

➤ *First, circle the words that describe what part of your body was touched. Then circle the words that describe what part of the abuser's body had contact with you. Draw a line from the part of the abuser's body that had contact with you to the part of your body that was touched. Finally, write a paragraph that would describe where the abuser touched you and with what part of his/her body.*

Your Body	*Abuser's Body*
Mouth	Mouth
Hands	Hands
Finger	Finger
Thighs	Thighs
Buttocks	Buttocks
Anus	Anus
Vagina	Vagina
Breasts	Breasts
Other	Penis
	Other

_____

_____

_____

_____

_____

_____

_____

_____

_____

_____

_____

_____

_____

➤ *What are you thinking after completing these exercises?*

_____

_____

_____

_____

_____

_____

_____

_____

_____

_____

_____

➤ *How are you feeling?*

_____

_____

_____

_____

_____

_____

_____

_____

_____

_____

_____

Exercise 4: More about What Happened

➤ *Pick an incident or two that happened after the first time. Pick something you feel it would be helpful to tell or that is a good example of what usually happened. Write about it in the space provided below.*

_____

_____

_____

_____

_____

_____

_____

_____

_____

_____

_____

_____

_____

_____

_____

_____

_____

_____

_____

_____

_____

_____

_____

_____

Exercise 5: The Worst

For many people who have been sexually abused, there are particular memories that they find too embarrassing to tell or too painful to remember. The long-term goal is for you to no longer carry the burden of sexual abuse secrets.

➤ *If, at this point, you are ready to begin discussing those most painful memories, you might begin by telling one experience of sexual abuse that you have previously not been able to talk about.*

_____

_____

_____

_____

_____

_____

_____

_____

_____

_____

_____

_____

_____

_____

_____

_____

_____

_____

_____

_____

_____

_____

_____

_____

_____

_____

_____

The Worst, continued

➤ *If you can go on to write about other experiences, please use this page.*

_____

_____

_____

_____

_____

_____

_____

_____

_____

_____

_____

_____

_____

_____

_____

_____

_____

_____

_____

_____

_____

_____

_____

_____

_____

Exercise 6: How Did It End?

➤ *What happened to make it end? Did you say something? Did someone find out without your telling? Did the offender tell? Did the circumstances change—perhaps because you or the offender moved away? Did something change that made it harder for the offender to abuse you and go unnoticed? Did your behavior let people know there was a problem without you actually having to say anything? Please describe.*

_____

_____

_____

_____

_____

_____

_____

_____

_____

_____

_____

_____

_____

_____

_____

_____

_____

_____

_____

_____

_____

_____

_____

_____

_____

_____

_____

_____

_____

In Their Own Words

It was one night when my father was drunk and he came into the room where my brother and I were sleeping. My mother was in her room sleeping. My father came in the room. I saw him walking toward me with his underwear and T-shirt on. I was pretending that I was asleep. I wouldn't move. I was feeling very scared. He got on top of me but I can't really remember if he stuck his penis or his fingers up in my vagina. I think he kept trying to wake me up, but I would not move. Sometimes I feel as if he's still holding me. Sometimes I do wish that he could put his arms around me and just hold me, telling me that everything is going to be okay. My heart is saying that I need him and I still love him but my mind-'n-body says, no, he might hurt you again. Now all I'm doing is turning to my mother for that love-'n-holdness. I need her right now, not my father. She's the only one I've got left to tell me that everything is going to be okay and that I will make it. My father betrayed me and everyone else.

Fear

Living in fear
is a terrible thing.
It's not fair
to be pulled by a string.
I feel like a puppet
being touched where it hurts.
They feel me all over
And rip off my shirt.
I'll never get over
This fear that I own;
I'll live in panic
And live like a stone.

Suggested Activities

- Write the details of the abuse that you most often remember.
- Write down the details of any new or recent memories of the abuse.
- Use the barometer from chapter IV to discuss where you would place yourself before you shared the details of your abuse and since you shared the details in therapy.
- On the Feelings List, circle the feelings that you had about telling the details before you shared them in therapy. Circle the feelings that you had while you were sharing the details. Then circle the feelings that you had after telling the details.

VIII. Was It Your Fault?

Many people who have been sexually abused blame themselves for some part of the abuse. They blame themselves for the things they think they should have done that they didn't do. They blame themselves for the things they did do that they think were wrong or bad. Most likely your therapist has told you that the abuse was not your fault, but that probably does not change the way you feel. Many people who have been sexually abused feel guilty about the abuse. *Guilt* is the painful feeling that comes when you are blaming yourself for doing something that you believe is wrong.

"I Should Have"

If you are feeling guilty about the abuse, you may be telling yourself that there are things you should have done differently.

➤ *Do you think there is something you should have done to prevent or stop the abuse? If you do, try to write about it in the space provided below.*

_____

_____

_____

_____

_____

It is hard enough if you are blaming yourself for the things you think you should have done. It may be even more painful if other people who are important to you are blaming you, too.

➤ *Has anyone told you that you should have done something to prevent or stop the abuse? If yes, who, and what have they said?*

_____

_____

_____

_____

_____

Here are some girls' comments about what they or others believe they should have done to prevent or stop the abuse.

"I should have fought him—I let it happen."

"I should have told my mother. Mom asked me why I didn't tell anybody. I was quiet and sneaky, trying to keep it a secret from everyone. I was afraid to get caught."

"He told me that if a girl doesn't want this sort of touch, she should say no or run away. Otherwise she must like it."

"She said, 'If he wasn't threatening you, why did you let him do it? Why didn't you run away?'"

Children and teenagers who have been sexually abused frequently feel guilty for not running, fighting, or telling. If you are feeling this way, it is important to remind yourself that the abuser was bigger, stronger, older, or had power or authority over you. When people experience a trauma, such as sexual abuse, they often freeze. They may try to convince themselves that the abuse isn't really happening to them by pretending to be asleep, or by trying to separate their thoughts and feelings from what is happening to their body, as though they are watching a movie. They may be unable to do anything but focus their energy on getting through the experience.

If you are feeling guilty about not telling sooner, it may be helpful to reread chapter V, "Keeping the Secret." Try to recall how the abuser convinced you to keep the abuse a secret and the fears that you had about telling. It is a sad fact that most children who are being sexually abused keep it a secret.

"What I Did Was Wrong"

There are many reasons why someone who has been sexually abused may believe that something she did was wrong or bad.

➤ *Are there things that make you believe the abuse was in some way your fault? If the answer is yes, use the space below to describe anything you did that makes you blame yourself for the abuse.*

_____

_____

_____

_____

_____

_____

_____

_____

_____

The abuser may have told you that the abuse was in some way your fault. Other people in your life may also have blamed you for doing something to cause the abuse.

➤ *Did the abuser say or do anything that made you feel like you were doing something wrong to cause the abuse? If the answer is yes, use the space below to explain.*

_____

_____

_____

_____

_____

_____

_____

➤ *Did anyone else tell you that you said or did anything that made some part of the abuse your fault? Please describe in the space below.*

_____

_____

_____

_____

_____

_____

_____

_____

_____

_____

_____

_____

_____

_____

We have listed below girls' comments about why they believe that something they did makes some part of the abuse their fault. These girls express thoughts and feelings that we have heard from many teenagers. Under each of their comments we have written our own response.

➤ *Please check the box if these are feelings you have had.*

☐ *"I loved him and I still do love him. Does that seem weird?"*

We frequently talk to girls who are confused about what part of the abuse was their fault because of their positive feelings for the person who abused them. Relationships between people are complicated. The abuser can be someone that a girl sometimes fears or hates and also someone that she loves and depends upon. The abuser may be the person who cared for her while others ignored or physically abused her. It may be that when the abuse was not happening the abuser was dependable or fun. Some girls have told us that the sexual abuse was part of their special relationship with the abuser. They were the one person who could make the abuser happy or meet his or her needs. When you love someone, you want their attention and enjoy the feeling that you have the ability to make them feel good.

If this reminds you of your situation, it is understandable if you still feel love toward the person who abused you. But the abuser is responsible for his or her actions. The abuser took advantage of your trust and love.

☐ *"I'm embarrassed about the stuff we did. Sometimes I liked the way it felt, physically."*

Many teenage girls express feeling guilty because they think that the kind of sexual contact they had with the abuser was especially bad. For instance some girls have said that they felt particularly guilty because the sexual contact included oral or anal sex or because the abuser was also female.

Girls have also been troubled by the fact that physical touch and sexual contact can feel good even in situations of sexual abuse. Some girls enjoyed the touch because it was the only way they got attention from anybody. They might have preferred a hug, a card game, a conversation, but the only way they could get the contact that they needed was through sexual contact. Other girls have said that they felt like their bodies betrayed them. In other words, they may have felt the touch was pleasant even through they didn't want it to happen.

Talking about the type of sexual contact and pleasurable sexual feelings you experienced during the abuse can be embarrassing. However, sharing these details in therapy can help you to understand your feelings and to blame yourself less.

☐ *"I liked the money, gifts, and special attention that I got. Sometimes, when I wanted money, I would even set myself up for the abuse."*

All children and teenagers enjoy receiving money, gifts, or special attention. That is why people who abuse children often offer them these things. Some girls who received money or bribes for the abuse have said that getting something in exchange made them feel more in control and less like a victim.

We have worked with other girls who described a destructive pattern that developed for them around receiving bribes for the abuse. After the abuse they would feel awful, but the bribes or money would allow them to feel better temporarily. They would then start to want the money or bribes that they could only get by being abused again. They began to feel like they were setting themselves up to be abused.

If you are troubled because you took bribes for the abuse, try to talk about it with your therapist. With support, you can put your part in the abuse into perspective. You don't need to keep guilty thoughts and feelings a secret anymore.

☐ *"He says I came on to him. I would always sit in his lap. It must be my fault."*

Some girls have come to believe the things that the abuser or others have said to blame them for the abuse. Children who have been sexually abused by an adult may be blamed for wanting a grown-up to show them affection. Girls who have been sexually abused may be blamed for flirting or dressing or acting sexy. Children and teenagers who have been sexually abused may be told that they are the ones who should have known better.

The clothing that a girl wears, flirting, and acting sexy are not responsible for the sexual abuse. In all situations of sexual abuse it is the abuser who is abusing his or her power over another person.

☐ *"I was old enough to know better."*

The control that some adults have over children does not stop at any particular age. It depends on the individuals involved. It may be especially difficult for an older child to get an adult to change something that has been going on for a long time. In other words, if a child has been abused since the age of five, she may feel no more able to stop the abuse when she is 14 than she felt when she was five.

Sexual abuse is always the fault of the abuser. In any situation between an adult and a child, regardless of the child's behavior, it is the adult who has more knowledge and experience and who must be responsible for making the decision that is best for the child.

More about Blame

Children and teenagers often feel blamed for the abuse because of the things that happen after they tell. They may have to answer questions about the details of the abuse from social workers, the police, or lawyers. Just having to remember and tell strangers what happened can make them feel at fault. If the abuser is a family member and the abuse is reported to the authorities, the child may be removed from her home. This generally occurs because of concerns about her safety or to try to protect her from the abuser. But this still means that she may have to leave her home, friends, and family.

Even though you have been sexually abused and other people believe you, you may not be able to prove you have been abused. Most cases of child sexual abuse do not go to trial, and most abusers do not serve time in jail. No wonder it can seem like the person who has been abused is being blamed and punished for the abuse, and not the abuser.

➤ *Do you have any additional thoughts about the abuse being your fault after reading this chapter? If you do, please write them in the space below.*

_____

_____

_____

_____

_____

Why does it sometimes seem like everyone, including yourself, wants to blame you for the abuse? Perhaps because it is very painful to admit to ourselves that adults do this sort of cruel thing to children—often to the children they live with; often to the children they love. It is human nature to avoid looking at things that are painful and upsetting. It would be easier if we could say that this child liked this or brought it upon herself, or that it didn't hurt her. It would be easier, but it wouldn't be true.

You may still feel that the abuse was your fault—or that some part of it was. Try to show yourself the compassion and empathy that you would show to a friend.

In Their Own Words

It's just not fair. I feel like I'm being punished when I didn't commit a crime.
So that's probably one of the reasons I feel like it's my fault.
Blaming myself is easy,
I can do it just like that.
But when I think about it
It's not a fact.
It's hard for me to deal with this
And sometimes not.
But then I think about it:
It's my fault.
Blame is one thing that really sucks.
I always feel blame towards myself even though I know that the truth is right in front of my face. I try to get rid of my blame, but sometimes it pushes back into you.
All you can do is try.
Sometimes I feel like I'm being punished. It wasn't my fault that I got raped! Sometimes I do blame myself. I feel like my heart is in many different broken pieces.

Love??!!

They told me they loved me
But now I know they don't.
Love is confusing to see
And I'm afraid I always won't.
I'm scared to love
Because I hurt so bad.
I wish I was a dove
That could fly like mad.
They hurt me outside
But that I can take;
It's the hurt inside
That makes me feel like
a mistake!

Suggested Activities

- Write a list of things you've heard other people say that have made you feel like the abuse was your fault.
- Write a poem about feeling that the abuse is your fault.
- Write a story about someone who thought the abuse was her fault.

IX. It's OK to Have Feelings

In chapter VII, "Telling the Details," we mentioned that it may be more difficult to remember and talk about your feelings about the abuse than to tell what happened. We've also discussed how people often freeze or numb their feelings to cope with the abuse. Some of you may be feeling numb or out of touch with most of your feelings as a result of trying to block the painful feelings connected to the sexual abuse. If you coped with the abuse by freezing, allowing yourself to feel may be hard. In the beginning you may feel less in control, and more unexpected memories may surface. It can be scary if you are dealing with your feelings about the abuse for the first time. Hopefully, you will find that once you let yourself experience these painful feelings, you are able to move on to feelings of happiness and hope.

Some of you may have the opposite problem from freezing or feeling numb. You may be overwhelmed and unable to control the flood of feelings. It can seem like your feelings are bursting out everywhere. You may have difficulty seeing how these feelings are related to the sexual abuse. However, it is likely that you will feel more in control if you are able to connect your feelings to the abuse.

Maybe you think that the feelings you are having about the abuse are stupid or wrong. You may think that you shouldn't feel what you are feeling, that you should have different feelings. Most people who have been sexually abused have confusing feelings, sometimes about the abuser, sometimes about people who they think should have protected them from the abuse, and sometimes about themselves.

Feelings Exercises

The exercises in this chapter are designed to help you identify and write about the difficult feelings that are connected to your experience of sexual abuse. The Feelings List at the front of the book may be helpful if you have trouble coming up with words for your feelings.

Exercise 1: Feelings about the Abuse

➤ *Fill in the blanks in the sentences below.*

I feel confused about _____

I feel angry at _____

I feel angry about _____

I feel betrayed by _____

I am worried that _____

I feel sorry for _____

I am afraid that _____

I love _____

I feel hurt by _____

I feel thankful for _____

I am ashamed of _____

I feel guilty about _____

I am sad that _____

I feel uncomfortable when _____

I feel hopeless when I think of _____

Exercise 2: Anger and Blame

Anger can be an unpleasant and uncomfortable feeling. People usually feel angry when they think someone has mistreated them. Sometimes part of being angry is wanting to fight back at the person who caused this feeling.

People who have been sexually abused are often angry at the person who they blame for the abuse. Sometimes they blame the abuser. Sometimes they blame another person. And sometimes they blame themselves.

➤ *Who do you feel angry at, and why?*

_____

_____

_____

_____

_____

➤ *Who do you blame for the abuse, and why do you blame them?*

_____

_____

_____

_____

_____

Exercise 3: Sadness and Loss

Sadness is an unhappy, dull, and heavy feeling. People often feel sad when they experience disappointment or loss and are without hope. Feelings of sadness can come and go, lasting for a brief period each time, or they can be experienced as a nearly constant mood. In the second case, a person is said to be depressed.

➤ *When and how often do you feel sad?*

_____

_____

_____

_____

_____

➤ *What do you think you have lost?*

_____

_____

_____

_____

_____

Exercise 4: Feelings of Shame

Shame is a very painful feeling of having lost the respect of other people because of something you have done. It is the feeling that something is wrong with you and that you are bad or worthless. The experience of sexual abuse can leave anyone with deep feelings of shame.

➤ *Below are other teenagers' descriptions of their feelings of shame because of sexual abuse. Check any of the feelings that you have also experienced.*

☐ "I feel like there is something wrong with me deep down inside."

☐ "When I think about the sexual abuse, I feel dirty."

☐ "If people knew about the things I have done, they would hate me. They wouldn't want to be my friend."

☐ "Do I wear some kind of a mark or sign on me that says 'abuse me'? It must be something about me that I keep on being abused."

➤ *Why do you think that people who have been sexually abused often feel this way?*

_____

_____

_____

_____

_____

Take a Break: Check In With Yourself

➤ *What are you thinking?*

_____

_____

_____

_____

_____

➤ *How are you feeling?*

_____

_____

_____

_____

More Exercises

Exercise 5: Feelings About the Abuser

Your feelings about the abuser will be affected by his or her relationship to you. If the abuser was a family member or someone you depended on, it is likely that you have very complicated feelings.

The questions below should help you to sort out your different feelings about the abuser. If you were abused by more than one person, answer these questions for each person.

➤ *How did you feel about the abuser before the abuse started?*

_____

_____

_____

_____

➤ *Did you ever have nice times with the abuser when the abuse wasn't happening? If so, what were they?*

_____

_____

_____

_____

➤ *When the abuse began, what did you think and feel about what was happening—and about the abuser?*

_____

_____

_____

_____

_____

➤ *As the abuse continued, did your feelings change? How?*

_____

_____

_____

_____

_____

➤ *How did you think the abuser felt about you?*

_____

_____

_____

_____

_____

➤ *What do you think and feel about the abuser now?*

_____

_____

_____

_____

_____

➤ *What, if anything, would you like to say to the abuser?*

_____

_____

_____

_____

_____

➤ *What, if anything, do you wish the abuser would say to you?*

_____

_____

_____

_____

_____

_____

_____

Exercise 6: The Other Person

There may have been another person in your life who you depended on or looked to for help. You may have hoped that this person would save you from the abuse, or felt that they were responsible for the abuse in some way. Some people who have been sexually abused have felt more angry at this person than at the abuser.

➤ *Was there a person like this in your situation? If so, who?*

_____

_____

_____

_____

_____

_____

➤ *How did you feel about this person before the abuse occurred?*

_____

_____

_____

_____

➤ *What did you think or feel about this person during the time of the abuse?*

_____

_____

_____

_____

_____

➤ *How do you think they felt about you?*

_____
_____
_____
_____
_____

➤ *Was there something you wished this person would have done to stop the abuse?*

_____
_____
_____
_____
_____

➤ *How do you feel about this person now?*

_____
_____
_____
_____
_____

➤ *What would you like to say to this person now?*

_____
_____
_____
_____
_____
_____
_____
_____
_____

Exercise 7: Feelings about Other Relationships

Sexual abuse can affect your feelings about relationships with other people besides those involved in the abuse. Often teenagers find themselves distrustful of adults, uncomfortable around people of the same sex as the abuser, worried that other children might be being abused, or embarrassed around people who know of the abuse.

➤ *How has the sexual abuse affected your relationships with other people?*

_____

_____

_____

_____

_____

Exercise 8: Connecting Your Feelings to the Abuse

Now it is time to try to connect your feelings to the abuse. Think back to the time you were being abused. How old were you? Remember how you acted? What did you look like? What clothes did you wear?

➤ *If it's hard to write about yourself, try referring to yourself as "she." What did she feel and think and wish for? (If you don't remember what she felt, say what you imagine she might have felt or thought.) Was she frightened and confused? When she cried, what was it about? Who did she want to comfort her? Tell how she felt about the abuse as clearly as you can.*

_____

_____

_____

_____

_____

_____

_____

_____

_____

_____

_____

_____

_____

_____

In Their Own Words

Some teenagers find that writing poetry can help them to express difficult feelings.

Crying and Trying

Crying so hard
in my secret room,
my heart pounding—
time to face my doom.
Hearing the laughter
of this evil man,
Crying much harder
because I'm in demand,
Trying so hard to get away,
pushing and kicking,
"I hate you," I say.

Trapped

I want to know
what is right,
what is wrong.
I see my image,
my reflection.
Is it me
or only an empty shell?
The hard part
lies in my soul.
No one can tell—
it is buried beneath
in pain and fear.
Trapped by my feelings,
Trapped with myself.
There is no escape.
Help me.
I'm falling.
I want to get out of this place.
Or is it me
myself
I'm trying to run from?

My Little Girl Inside

All alone,
nobody to turn to,
this little girl inside is dying,
all her suffering and pain is being dug
up from her grave.
Overwhelming as may be, her outer person
is trying to stay in focus with the
present,
she wants to be free from all that's
happened,
but feels as though she will never be.
she is me.

There Is Pain

There's a pain in my heart
That runs very deep.
It haunts me through day,
It haunts me in sleep.
The dreams that I dream,
The terror I feel,
Remind me of memories
So painfully real.
The touch of his hands,
the abuse done to me,
Ten years of hell
That she didn't see.

It tears me apart
To feel so alone,
Without any hope,
No place to call home.
Needing assurance
that I did no wrong—
Then maybe I'll find it,
The will to go on.

Confusion

I am so confused and
I don't understand it;
I want to live but
yet I die.
I want to love but
Yet I hate,
Confusion, why?
I want the help but
yet I run.
I want people to see but
yet blind them.
I want to stay but
yet I leave.
So confused but
Yet I block it out.
So please, please
Tell me
Why, oh Why confusion?

Suggested Activities

- Write a letter to the abuser. You don't have to send it, but it's a good way to get out some of your feelings.
- Write a letter to the other person.
- Write what you now, as a teenager, want to say to the abused child who was you. What might you want to tell her?
- Make a list of the people whose relationship to you has been affected by the sexual abuse. Talk or write about how each of these relationships has been affected.
- Use the Feelings List:
    - Circle the feelings that best describe how you felt as a child.
    - Circle the feelings that you have about the abuser; about the other person.
    - Circle any feelings you have had today; that you had this week.
- Make a Feelings Book. Draw a picture to go with each of the feelings that you experience most often.
- Make a collage about your feelings.

X. Taking Charge of Your Life

You have reached the last chapter of this workbook. Because you have been willing to face and deal with your past, it is possible for you to gain control over how the abuse affects you in the future. In this chapter we look at ways in which you can take charge of your life: by being assertive, putting the sexual abuse in its place, recognizing your strengths, and getting and giving support.

Being Assertive

In the last chapter, "It's OK to Have Feelings," you looked at some of the ways your experience of sexual abuse is affecting your present relationships. You have also learned in earlier chapters that the sexual abuse was a trauma, a painful experience that you could not control or stop. The abuser did not care about your feelings or what you wanted or needed. It is possible that in your relationships today you still don't expect other people to care about what you feel or want. Or maybe, as a result of the abuse, you think that the only way to get what you want in life is to be controlling of other people and ignore their feelings.

Some people who have been abused think that it doesn't help to stand up for yourself and tell people what you're feeling. As a result, they may not be willing to assert themselves. When people are passive in relationships, they act like their feelings and needs aren't as important as the other person's. They often put themselves down and don't show their true feelings. It is most important to them to please other people and avoid disagreements. People who are passive have trouble saying no. They often end up feeling taken advantage of and mistreated in relationships—just like they were by the abuser.

Other people who have been abused think that in order to get what you want in a relationship you must try to gain power over the other person. They take an aggressive approach to relationships. When people are being aggressive, they act like the only way to get what they want is by using force, by threatening, or by being sneaky. They put their feelings before the other person's and try to control people.

When people have been abused as children, they often need to learn that they can have fair and equal relationships. You can learn to be assertive. Being assertive means:

- Doing things that are good for you in relationships
- Sticking up for what you want and need
- Showing your true feelings
- Respecting the other person's feelings
- Being fair

How would you rate yourself? In your relationships with friends or sexual partners, are you passive? Do you put their feelings first, so you have difficulty saying no and standing up for yourself? Are you aggressive—controlling other people, putting your needs and feelings above theirs? Or are you assertive? In your relationships, do you show your feelings and stand up for yourself in a way that is fair to yourself and the other person?

Where would you place yourself on this scale of one to ten?

1	5	10
Passive	**Assertive**	**Aggressive**

I rate myself _____ on the scale.

If you are often either passive or aggressive, you can learn to be assertive. In therapy you can discuss situations in which you did not act assertively. You can figure out how what you were feeling and thinking affected how you acted. You can set goals and plan how to be more assertive in the future. The sexual abuse doesn't have to continue to affect your relationships in the present. You have choices about the way you want to relate to people. We have used the Assertiveness Log on the next page to help girls in therapy learn how to be assertive and take charge of their own lives. Make copies of the log so you can use it over and over.

Assertiveness Log

Situation: _____

_____

_____

People: _____

_____

_____

Problem: _____

_____

_____

What I did: _____

_____

_____

What others did: _____

_____

_____

How it ended: _____

_____

_____

I was feeling: _____

_____

_____

I thought: _____

_____

_____

Did it work, and at what cost? _____

_____

_____

Next time I want to: _____

_____

_____

Putting the Abuse in Its Place

> "It seems as though you try so hard to remember the bad things that you forget some of the good."

You can work so hard at remembering and dealing with your sexual abuse that for a while it seems like the most important thing that ever happened to you. After all of your hard work, you are now at the point where it is important to remind yourself that the abuse was just one part of your life. You don't want to forget the good memories. The following exercises were designed to help you put the abuse in its place, by helping you to remember the good things.

Exercise 1: Your Favorite Place

➤ *Describe your favorite place. Write at least one good memory of something that happened in this place.*

_____

_____

_____

_____

Exercise 2: A Favorite Activity

➤ *Describe a favorite activity. Write one good memory about doing this activity.*

_____

_____

_____

_____

Exercise 3: A Caring Adult

➤ *Tell about one adult who has been good to you.*

_____

_____

_____

_____

Exercise 4: A Special Friend

➤ *Describe a special friend. Write one good memory about some time that you spent together.*

_____

_____

_____

_____

Recognizing Your Strengths

In this workbook we have talked a lot about how being sexually abused can make you feel bad about yourself. Another effect of the sexual abuse may have been that you stopped doing activities you are good at and you enjoy. Part of putting the sexual abuse in its place is recognizing your strengths and doing more of the things that make you feel good about yourself. The exercises below are to help you recognize your strengths.

Exercise 1: Identifying Strengths

➤ *List 10 things that you are good at:*

1. _____
2. _____
3. _____
4. _____
5. _____
6. _____
7. _____
8. _____
9. _____
10. _____

➤ *List the five things that you like most about yourself:*

1. _____
2. _____
3. _____
4. _____
5. _____

Exercise 2: Giving Yourself Credit for Your Courage

➤ *What strengths have you developed as a result of facing and dealing with the abuse?*

_____

_____

_____

_____

_____

Exercise 3: Favorite Activities

In the first column make a list of your 10 favorite things to do. In the second column record when you last did each activity. In the third column write when you plan to do this activity again.

➤ *Activity*

1. _____ 6. _____
2. _____ 7. _____
3. _____ 8. _____
4. _____ 9. _____
5. _____ 10. _____

➤ *Last Did*

1. _____ 6. _____
2. _____ 7. _____
3. _____ 8. _____
4. _____ 9. _____
5. _____ 10. _____

➤ *Plan to Do Again*

1. _____ 6. _____
2. _____ 7. _____
3. _____ 8. _____
4. _____ 9. _____
5. _____ 10. _____

Getting and Giving Support

Taking charge of your own life doesn't mean that you have to go it alone. As a matter of fact, knowing how and when to ask others for help is an important part of taking charge and living to the fullest. Hopefully, therapy has helped you learn to understand yourself better and to feel more in control. At different times throughout your life, you may want to use therapy as a place to learn more about yourself, solve personal problems, or set goals for your future. If you would like to try to improve your present relationships with family members, you might want to talk to your therapist about family therapy.

Perhaps you have also learned about building trusting relationships with people. You no longer need to feel isolated and different from other people because of the abuse. If you haven't already joined a survivors group, a group for people who have been sexually abused, you might find this helpful. A survivors group can be a place to receive support and give support to others who have been through experiences similar to yours.

You have a lot to give! Your courage and strength in facing your abuse can be an inspiration to others who are beginning this work. Because of all the hard work that you have done, you are a role model for other teenagers who have been abused. Like the celebrities we mentioned in the beginning of this book who have spoken publicly about their abuse, you, too, have broken the silence. You, too, can help others to both understand and overcome the effects of sexual abuse.

Congratulations for completing this workbook. We admire the courage and strength that you have shown in taking charge of your life.

In Their Own Words

In Time Perhaps

In time

perhaps

my wounds will heal

And my pain will no longer be numb.

It will disappear.

The smile that I wear upon my face

will be real.

My locked up dreams

will slowly

cut themselves free

from helplessness and disappointment.

Suggested Activities

- Set at least two goals to help yourself become more assertive. Describe what you will do to reach these goals.
- Take a book on assertiveness training out of the library and read it.
- Make a list of people who you admire or consider role models. Describe why you admire them.
- Write about your hopes for the future.
- Draw a picture, make a collage, or write a poem about hope.
- Write about what you hope to be doing one year from now; two years from now.
- If you are not a member of a survivors' group and you want to learn more about these groups, call your local women's center and ask them about groups for people who have been sexually abused.
- Talk to your therapist about how group therapy or family therapy might be helpful to you.

About the Authors

Lulie Munson, LICSW, has worked for 10 years as a psychotherapist at the Germaine Lawrence School, a residential treatment program for troubled adolescent girls. Lulie co-founded the Germaine Lawrence Survivors Group and leads the group together with Karen Riskin.

Karen Riskin, LICSW, is the Deputy Executive Director of Germaine Lawrence, Inc. She and Lulie Munson have presented workshops on their work with adolescent survivors at conferences throughout New England.